THE MYSTERIOUS CITY OF EL NUMERO

Solve the puzzles,
save the world!

ARCTURUS

ARCTURUS

This edition published in 2020 by Arcturus Publishing Limited
26/27 Bickels Yard, 151–153 Bermondsey Street,
London SE1 3HA

Author: William Potter
Illustrator: Rayanne Vieira
Editors: Sebastian Rydberg, Joe Harris, and Julia Adams
Designers: Amy McSimpson and Elaine Wilkinson

ISBN: 978-1-83940-323-1
CH008098NT
Supplier 33, Date 0220, Print run 9659

Printed in China

What is STEM?

STEM is a world-wide initiative
that aims to cultivate an
interest in Science, Technology,
Engineering, and Mathematics,
in an effort to promote these
disciplines to as wide a variety of
students as possible.

HOW TO USE THIS BOOK

This exciting, interactive adventure story features puzzles on every page. When you reach a puzzle, stop! You must "unlock" the next part of the story by solving that problem. Don't skip ahead until you've worked out an answer! Check that your solution is correct by turning to the back of the book.

It's worth having some scrap paper and some tracing paper handy for any working out. Give each puzzle your best shot, and don't worry if you get some answers wrong first time—you can still carry on with the story and try again later.

HAPPY ADVENTURING!

MEET DARING EXPLORERS DAISY AND DALE DEED

When sister and brother Daisy and Dale Deed receive a gift from their missing father, it leads them on a journey over rough seas, to face hair-raising tests that will solve the mystery of El Numero.

Siblings Daisy and Dale Deed are wiser than their young years might suggest. After their mother passed away, their father, the historian and adventurer Professor Darren Deed, raised them on his own. He taught them ancient history, geography, and mathematics, until he left on a mission to South America, and was never seen again.

DAISY DEED

DALE DEED

CAPTAIN CAMILA

Captain Camila is a brave sea captain and old friend of Professor Deed. Famed for her solo crossing of the infamous Savage Straits, she retired from competitive yacht racing to work as a skipper for hire in the notorious port of Santa Luna.

A year after their father's disappearance, Daisy and Dale receive a mysterious parcel in the mail. Hurriedly unwrapping it, they find a pocket watch inside. "Didn't this belong to Dad?" asks Dale.

"I think there's something inside it!" says Daisy, struggling with the clasp. "Give it here—I'll do it," says Dale. However, he soon gives up, looking red-faced. Daisy bursts out laughing.

Then Dale remembers something. "The portrait!" In the living room of their home hangs a painting, showing their dad holding the very same watch. "There's the watch—and there are three clocks, too!"

I think there's a clue to opening it in the painting.

That would be typical of Dad!

"The title of the painting is 'From Noon Till Night.'" says Daisy. "Perhaps we should turn the hands on the watch to point to the four times in the painting, in the the right order." Can you help them?

5

With the correct turns, the watch cover pops open. There aren't any cogs inside. Instead it holds a folded, hand-drawn map. The map shows the location of a mysterious South American island, El Numero. Dale tries to look it up in an atlas, but the island doesn't seem to exist!

Could Dad have made a mistake?

Each square on the map represents 4 nautical miles. Prof Deed's notes say El Numero is 12 nautical miles west of Devil's Deep, 8 nautical miles toward Wreckage Reef, 8 nautical miles farther west, then 20 nautical miles north. Reading first by column, then by row, at what coordinates should El Numero be found?

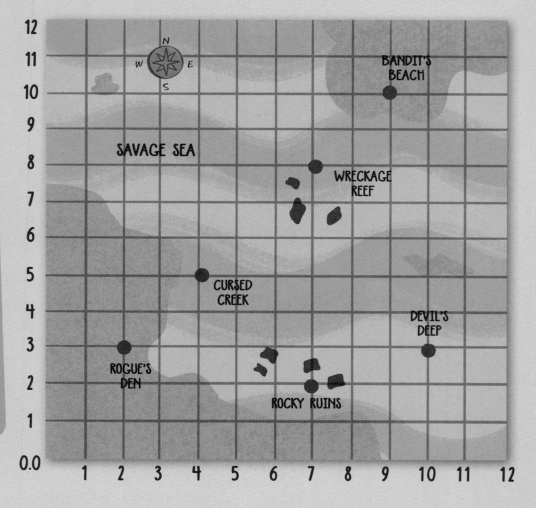

The island of El Numero is not marked on the map,
but Daisy and Dale decide to look for it anyway.

Having raised the money for flights and boat hire, the siblings head to the airport and look at the schedules.

FROM	TO	LEAVING	FLIGHT TIME
Townton	Miami	8:30am	6 hours
Miami	Star City	?	$4\frac{1}{2}$ hours
Star City	Santa Luna	?	2 hours

We need to catch these three connecting flights to reach Santa Luna.

Santa Luna is eight hours ahead of Townton, where they are setting out from. If they have one hour between each flight landing and the next taking off, what will the local time be when they arrive in Santa Luna?

Daisy and Dale arrive at Santa Luna, feeling very tired! They are met by a man who claims to be the boat captain they hired. He offers them a lift to the dock where his boat is moored.

757946

497655

984765

565739

I'm sure we hired a boat with digits that add up to 37 ...

Do any of the boats at the dock have a number to match Daisy's description?

Assuming it's their mistake, Dale and Daisy get aboard the man's boat.
Some way out to sea, he demands their map.
"I'll take that as my payment for your safe voyage," he says,
"That is, unless you'd rather get off here!"
"There are sharks! We'd get eaten alive!" cries Dale.
"Don't worry," says the captain. "I'll restore the map to its owners."

I am a guardian of the sacred island of El Numero. No strangers are allowed there! I have been guarding the island since I was 18. My father, too. He was guardian for 37 years before me. I am 43 now. In ten years' time I will pass my father's record.

Check the captain's mathematics. Is he telling the truth?

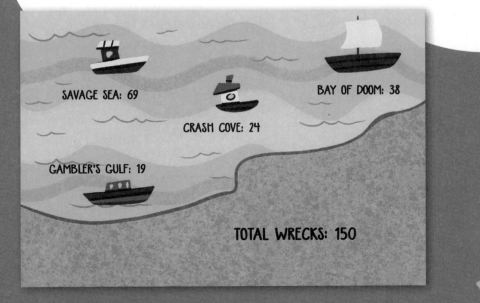

Daisy and Dale take their chances in the sea. Luckily, the sharks turn out to be dolphins! As the captain's boat sails out of view, a second boat appears, and the Deeds wave to get its attention. Getting alongside, the captain of the new boat helps them aboard. "Strange place to go for a swim," she jokes. Daisy gives the captain a hard stare and grabs a towel. "We were forced into the water by our captain," she says.

"That wasn't your captain," says the boatswoman. "I am." She introduces herself as Captain Camila. "I was late reaching the airport, and couldn't stop that villain leading you away. I gave chase in my boat."

Dale explains their plan. "I've heard legends of El Numero and its countless treasures," says Captain Camila. "It's said to be in the Savage Sea, but too many ships have been wrecked there." Camila shows her new passengers a chart.

SAVAGE SEA: 69

CRASH COVE: 24

BAY OF DOOM: 38

GAMBLER'S GULF: 19

TOTAL WRECKS: 150

Look at the chart for the accidents in the local seas. What percentage of the accidents happened in the Savage Sea?

"Your father tried to hire me for this same voyage," says Camila. "You knew our dad?" asks Dale. Camila nods. "He contacted me a week before he disappeared. I'll help you find the island, and hopefully your father, too. But first we need a course … "

Daisy and Dale try to remember enough details to get them to the island.

Using tracing paper, work out the destination on the map from their start point. The boat heads north for 3 hours, then east for $1\frac{1}{2}$ hours, turning south for $\frac{1}{2}$ hour, then east for 2 hours, then north for 1 hour, then west for $\frac{1}{2}$ hour. Each map square is 4 knots across. If the boat sails at exactly 16 knots an hour, where will it end up on the map?

The going is good for a while, before the boat enters rough seas and the hull hits a rock, springing a leak. While the captain hurries to make a repair, Daisy and Dale need to bail out water.

Faster! Faster!

Water is getting into the boat at a rate of 4 cups a second. Each bucket can hold 10 cups. How many buckets of water must the kids bail from the boat every minute to stop the situation getting worse?

After repairs and a nervous, sleepless night, the Deeds wake to find the captain steering through a thick mist. She has to go slow to avoid number-shaped rocks.

"The locals say it's safest to sail around these rocks in a special pattern," she says. Plot a route showing them in ascending order.

Suddenly, there is a bump, but it's not a rock they've hit. Daisy and Dale look over the side of the boat. "It's wreckage!" says Dale. Daisy recognizes it. "It's what's left of that mean sailor's boat—the one who stole our map!" "Serves him right!" says Dale, though he is glad there is no sign of the man.

Then, a spooky island appears in front of them, emerging from the fog. Camila steers the boat around the coastline to find a safe place to weigh anchor.

Land ahoy!

The island has a coastline that is 200 boat lengths long with 40 boat lengths of cliffs, 30 boat lengths of jagged rocks, 80 boat lengths surrounded by reefs, and the rest by beaches. What percentage of the coast is beach?

Mooring off a beach, the trio begin exploring the island. There are pawprints on a path, perhaps belonging to some savage animal, but there's no other route, so they follow. Without weapons, Captain Camila arms herself with a flare pistol.

There are numbered stakes along the way, leading in different directions. Each bears a skull with a painted number. Many skulls are fanged. It feels like a warning. Dale points out that, while some skulls face toward them, others face stakes farther ahead on the path.

They are following a number sequence!

The first numbers in the sequence are 1, 2, 4, 7, 11. What is the pattern, and what four numbers come next?

The stakes lead to the entrance of a dark cave. Camila tries to rub sticks together to make a flame, but the wood is too damp, and she isn't very good at it. "I'm a sailor!" she laments. The trio prepare to enter the darkness using touch to find their way.

Painted on the cave entrance are symbols that might help guide them. The symbols are images of feet pointing in different directions—ahead, left, right, and back. Each foot has a number on it. "I think these show the number of steps we should take in each direction," says Daisy.

The feet show steps in the following directions: 6 Ahead, 3 Right, 4 Ahead, 2 Left, 3 Back, 1 Left, 5 Ahead, 2 Right, 2 Back, 1 Left, 5 Ahead. Simplify the route so you can reach the end point by moving just ahead, then right. How many steps need they take in each direction?

As they feel their way in the darkness, they hear growling that makes them shiver. They recall the footprints and skulls. Daisy reminds Camila of her flare gun. The captain nods in the dark and replies, "Close your eyes for a second." She fires the flare into the darkness, and glimpses an animal as it runs away down a side tunnel. She also spies a wooden door just ahead. When they get near, Camila says, "There's one lock but eight keys! Which one do we use?" Daisy has an answer. "We need to use all eight, but in the right order!"

START LOW   GO HIGH

2.2 2^2 0.5   0.25   1/3   4.5   5/4   1.2

The door has one lock but eight keys. The keys are numbered with decimals and fractions. To open the door, they need to use the keys in the order from the lowest number to the highest. What is the order?

The door is opened and the trio gasp. They are inside a high-ceilinged, candlelit room, decorated with carvings, paintings, and tapestries covered in numbers, symbols, and equations. They now know for sure they are within the walls of the Temple of El Numero. The path ahead is over numbered hexagonal stones. Dale shrieks. Next to the path is a skeleton. "It looks like he's been dead for a very long time!" Daisy says. "The skeleton is pointing ahead to the number 108, but why that number?"

Dale is less scared now.
He sees a pattern ...

The skeleton points to the number 108. Follow the times table that includes this number, stepping only on touching stones.

90 84 92 94 110 108 88 80
82 77 82 81 102 99 72 76
70 63 72 80 90 72 64 56
54 52 56 49 42 48 40
45 36 35 28 32
35 27 21 16 24
28 14 13 16 8
19 18 7 6 5
9

We need to start
from the first number
in that times table.

Once they reach the other side, the door opens to reveal a long corridor. Dale hears a growling sound behind them, so they pick up the pace. They dash through another door, but this one seems to be stuck in the open position! How can they close it before the creature catches up?

Lock the door quickly!

How?

The door closes by the use of weights. There are three balances beside the door, with different combinations of stones. How many stones from the pile are needed to balance the bottom set?

With the balance set, the door closes behind them. After a brief rest,
the trio decide to proceed deeper into El Numero.
They enter a corridor with a series of statues along one wall.
Each statue is from a different age.

The first statue is dated 2673. The final one is dated 3761.
How many years are there between them?
2019 is 3761 in the El Numero calendar, what year was 2673?

The kids now know that El Numero is much older than they thought. What is its purpose? They enter a large echoing chamber with columns, a gallery, and hanging braziers, decorated with numbers and equations, many far beyond Daisy and Dale's knowledge of mathematics. Dale is about to speak when Daisy tells him to shush. They hear footsteps coming from the corridor behind them … and growling! The beast is still tracking them. Dale spots a large closet they may be able to hide inside.

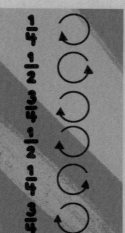

Opening the lock on the closet requires a series of turns, first one way, then the other. What position will it be in once all the turns are followed?

The trio opens the closet, but it is too full of ceremonial gowns to squeeze into. The creature has them cornered! Suddenly they hear: "Digit! Leave!" Revealed in the light, the creature is a dog. It trots over to its master, who steps out from the shadows. "Dad!" cry the children. Indeed, it is Professor Deed, now with a beard. He hugs them and thanks Captain Camila.
"This is Digit," says the professor, pointing to the dog.
It licks the children's hands.
"You shouldn't have followed me," he tells his kids. "It's not safe!"
"Then why did you leave us a clue?" asks Daisy.
"I wanted you to know I was alive," says her father,
"not risk all to rescue me." He reveals how he found El Numero,
by drawing a diagram on the dusty floor.

The professor had unearthed an ancient tile with five numbers missing. These were map distances. All the rows and columns and diagonals of three squares in the square should add up to 15. What are the missing numbers?

2	9	?
?	?	?
6	?	8

While happy to be reunited with his children, the professor looks sad, and reveals the reason why. "I'm so relieved to see you," he says, "but they won't let me leave." He unbuttons his shirt to reveal a talisman around his neck. The symbols on the talisman add up to a secret number, the number that means he must remain.

What is the professor's number? It's represented by the letter "N" in all the clues.

$$N < 4^2$$
$$N > 3^2$$
$$N \text{ is odd.}$$
$$N < 3 \times 5$$
$$N > XI$$

The head guardian of El Numero enters the room and greets the professor by his number. He turns to the new arrivals. "You passed the number tests to enter El Numero," he says. "Well done!" The kids smile, but then the guardian says, "Now you must all remain here ... forever!" Captain Camila quickly grabs the children and tries to escape, but the exit is blocked by guards.

"The outside world can never learn the secrets of El Numero," says the guardian. The family and Captain Camila are led into the main council chamber, where 11 other guardians are assembled. The head explains that El Numero was built to protect the ancient mathematics, to ensure numbers always add up to the same results. "Don't they always add up to the same results?" wonders Dale, but Daisy nudges him to be quiet. She doesn't want them to get into more trouble.

I am the 22nd head guardian, in my final year. Since El Numero was built, every head guardian has spent exactly 50 years keeping El Numero secret.

How many years is it since El Numero was built?

25

Since ancient times, the guardians of El Numero have formed a Prime Number Council of 13. When Professor Deed happened upon the island they had just lost one member. The professor agreed to remain. "I wasn't given a choice!" whispered the professor to his children. Daisy looked thoughtful, then spoke up.

If prime numbers are important, why not form two Prime Number Councils, using a total of 12 members instead of 13, so my father could go free?

How can 12 be split into two prime numbers?

The guardians mutter to each other, then agree to this revolutionary idea—perhaps they should consider inviting youngsters to join their council! The kids worry they will be forced to stay after all, but the head guardian agrees to free their father from his duties.

With your father free to watch over you, I trust you, and the boat captain, to swear an oath never to reveal details of El Numero.

The oath the visitors must swear is a mathematical promise. They must remove four numbers from those chosen by the guardian to leave a total of 50. Which four numbers do they remove from 3, 8, 11, 15, 23, 31, 33?

The Deed family and Captain Camila sail away from the island toward Santa Luna and the way home. Daisy ponders aloud, "All the legends of El Numero spoke of treasure hidden at its heart, but what was it?"

I can answer that with one final puzzle! If A is 1 and Z is 26, what is 6, 1, 13, 9, 12, 25?

What treasure did the children find in El Numero? Gold? Diamonds?

ANSWERS

PAGE 5

Dale and Daisy wind the hands of the pocket watch to …
12:10,
then 8:40,
then 10:05,
and finally 10:45.

PAGE 6

El Numero should be at coordinates 5, 10.

PAGE 7

They sell the items worth $120, $270, $310, and $400.

PAGE 8

The flight from Townton to Miami arrives at 2:30pm (Townton time). The flight from Miami to Star City leaves at 3:30pm and arrives at 8pm (Townton time). The flight from Star City to Santa Luna leaves at 9pm and arrives at 11pm (Townton time, again). Because Santa Luna is 8 hours ahead, it is now 7am local time.

PAGE 9

No. The boats have digits that add up to 38, 36, 39, and 35.

PAGE 10

No, the captain would beat his father's record in 12 years, not ten. He is not who he claims to be.

PAGE 11

46%

PAGE 12

The boat sails 12 squares north, 6 east, 2 south, 8 east, 4 north and 2 west.

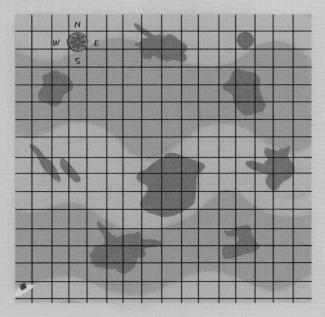

PAGE 13

60 x 4 ÷ 10 = 24 buckets of water.

PAGE 14

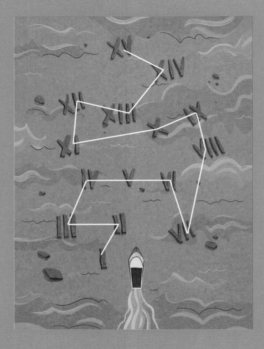

PAGE 15

25%.

PAGE 16

The difference between the numbers increases by 1 each time. Numbers next in the sequence are: 16, 22, 29, 37.

PAGE 17

15 steps ahead, 1 step to the right.

PAGE 18

From lowest to highest, the order is 0.25, 1/3, 0.5, 1.2, 5/4, 2.2, 2^2, 4.5.

PAGE 19

The route follows the 9 times table, so the route is 9, 18, 27, 36, 45, 54, 63, 72, 81, 90, 99, 108.

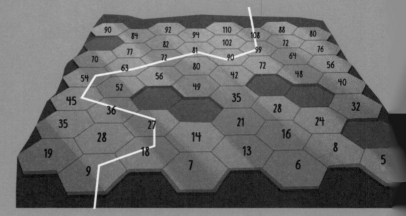

PAGE 20

The balance needs seven stones.

PAGE 21

1088. If 3761 is 2019, 2673 was 931.

PAGE 22

PAGE 23

PAGE 24

13.

PAGE 25

1,100.

PAGE 26

5 and 7.

PAGE 27

The group must remove 3, 15, 23, and 33. This leaves 8 + 11 + 31 = 50.

PAGE 28

The letters of the alphabet have been replaced by numbers in order from 1 to 26, so 6, 1, 13, 9, 12, 25 = F.A.M.I.L.Y.

31

GLOSSARY

BRAZIER A metal pan, holding coals or candles.

DECIMAL A fraction with tenths shown as numbers after a dot, for example 1/2 = 0.5.

KNOT A unit of speed used at sea. One knot equals one nautical mile per hour.

NAUTICAL MILE A unit used to measure distance at sea. One nautical mile is a little longer than one "standard" mile.

PRIME NUMBER A number that can only be divided by itself and 1.

FURTHER INFORMATION

Fitzgerald, Theresa. *Math Dictionary for Kids: The #1 Guide For Helping Kids With Math*. Waco (TX), USA: Prufrock Press, 2016.

Goldsmith, Mike. *How to Be a Math Genius: Your Brilliant Brain and How to Train It*. London, UK: DK Children, 2012.

INDEX